# NURSERY RHYMES

Illustrated by Gill Guile

**Brown Watson**
ENGLAND
© 2010 Brown Watson, England

# CONTENTS

First published 2010 by Brown Watson,
The Old Mill, 76 Fleckney Road,
Kibworth Beauchamp, Leics, LE8 0HG

ISBN: 978-0-7097-9927-6

# Jack and Jill

Jack and Jill went up the hill
To fetch a pail of water.
Jack fell down and broke his crown,
And Jill came tumbling after.

4

Up Jack got, and home did trot
As fast as he could caper;
He went to bed to mend his head
With vinegar and brown paper.

## Little Jack Horner

Little Jack Horner
Sat in the corner,
Eating a Christmas pie;
He put in his thumb,
And pulled out a plum,
And said 'What a good boy am I!'

## Tom the Piper's Son

Tom Tom the piper's son,
Stole a pig and away did run;
The pig was eat, and Tom was beat,
And Tom went howling down the street.

6

# Georgie Porgie

Georgie Porgie, pudding and pie,
Kissed the girls and made them cry.
When the boys came out to play,
Georgie Porgie ran away.

# Jack be Nimble

Jack be nimble,
Jack be quick,
Jack jump over
The candlestick.

# Baa Baa Black Sheep

Baa baa black sheep, have you any wool?
Yes, sir, yes, sir, three bags full!
One for the master, one for the dame,
And one for the little boy who lives
Down the lane.

# Old King Cole

Old King Cole was a merry old soul,
And a merry old soul was he;
He called for his pipe, and he called for his bowl,
And he called for his fiddlers three.
Every fiddler had a fine fiddle,
And a very fine fiddle had he;
Oh, there's none so rare,
As can compare
With King Cole and his fiddlers three.

# Mary, Mary

Mary, Mary, quite contrary,
How does your garden grow?
With silver bells,
And cockle shells,
And pretty maids all in a row.

# Incy Wincy Spider

Incy Wincy Spider climbed up the water spout.

Down came the rain and washed the spider out.

Out came the sun and dried up all the rain,

And Incy Wincy Spider climbed

Up the spout again!

# Two Little Dicky Birds

Two little dicky birds

Sitting on a wall,

One named Peter, one named Paul.

Fly away Peter, fly away Paul,

Come back Peter, come back Paul!

# One, Two, Buckle My Shoe

One, two, buckle my shoe;
Three, four, knock at the door;
Five, six, pick up sticks;
Seven, eight, lay them straight;
Nine, ten, my fat hen;
Eleven, twelve, dig and delve;
Thirteen, fourteen, maids a-courting;
Fifteen, sixteen, maids in the kitchen;
Seventeen, eighteen, maids in waiting;
Nineteen, twenty, my plate's empty.

# See-Saw Margery Daw

See-saw Margery Daw,

Jacky shall have a new master;

Jacky shall earn but a penny a day,

Because he can't work any faster.

# Half a Pound of Tuppenny Rice

Half a pound of tuppenny rice,

Half a pound of treacle,

That's the way the money goes,

Pop goes the weasel!

13

# Boys and Girls, Come Out to Play

Boys and girls, come out to play,

The moon doth shine as bright as day.

Leave your supper, and leave your sleep,

And come with your playfellows into the street.

Come with a whoop and come with a call,

Come with a good will, or not at all.

Up the ladder and down the wall,

A halfpenny loaf will serve us all;

You find the milk, and I'll find the flour,

And we'll have a pudding

In half-an-hour.

14

15

## Star Light

Star light, star bright,
The first star I see tonight,
I wish I may, I wish I might,
Have the wish I wish tonight.

## Rock-a-Bye Baby

Rock-a-bye baby on the tree top,
When the wind blows the cradle will rock,
When the bough breaks
The cradle will fall,
And down will come baby,
Cradle and all.

# The Queen of Hearts

The Queen of Hearts
She made some tarts,
All on a summer's day;
The Knave of Hearts,
He stole the tarts,
And took them right away.

The King of Hearts
Called for the tarts,
And beat the Knave full sore;
The Knave of Hearts
Brought back the tarts,
And vowed he'd steal no more.

# There Was an Old Woman

There was an old woman who lived in a shoe,
She had so many children, she didn't know what to do!
So she gave them some broth without any bread,
And she whipped them all soundly,
And sent them to bed!

# Little Polly Flinders

Little Polly Flinders
Sat among the cinders,
Warming her pretty little toes.

Her mother came and caught her,
And whipped her little daughter
For spoiling her nice new clothes.

# Wee Willie Winkie

Wee Willie Winkie runs through the town,
Upstairs and downstairs in his nightgown,
Rapping at the window and crying through the lock,
Are all the children in bed, it's past eight o'clock?

19

# Mary Had a Little Lamb

Mary had a little lamb,
Its fleece was white as snow,
And everywhere that Mary went,
That lamb was sure to go.

It followed her to school one day,
That was against the rule;
It made the children laugh and play,
To see a lamb at school.

# Old Mother Hubbard

Old Mother Hubbard
Went to the cupboard,
To give the poor dog a bone;
But when she got there,
The cupboard was bare,
And so the poor dog had none.

# Hot Cross Buns

Hot cross buns! Hot cross buns!
One a penny, two a penny,
Hot cross buns!
If you have no daughters,
Give them to your sons.
One a penny, two a penny,
Hot cross buns!

# I Saw a Ship A-Sailing

I saw a ship a-sailing,
A-sailing on the sea,
And oh, it was all laden
With pretty things for thee!

There were comfits in the cabin,
And apples in the hold.
The sails were made of silk,
And the masts were made of gold.

The four and twenty sailors
That stood between the decks
Were four and twenty white mice
With chains about their necks.

The captain was a duck
With a packet on his back,
And when the ship began to move,
The captain said, "Quack! Quack!"

23

# Ride a Cock Horse

Ride a cock horse to Banbury Cross,

To see a fine lady upon a white horse;

With rings on her fingers and bells on her toes,

She shall have music wherever she goes.

# Rain, Rain, Go Away

Rain, rain, go away,
Come again another day,

All the children want to play;
Rain, rain, go to Spain,
Never show your face again.

# Hickory, Dickory Dock

Hickory, dickory dock,
The mouse ran up the clock.
The clock struck one,
The mouse ran down,
Hickory, dickory dock.

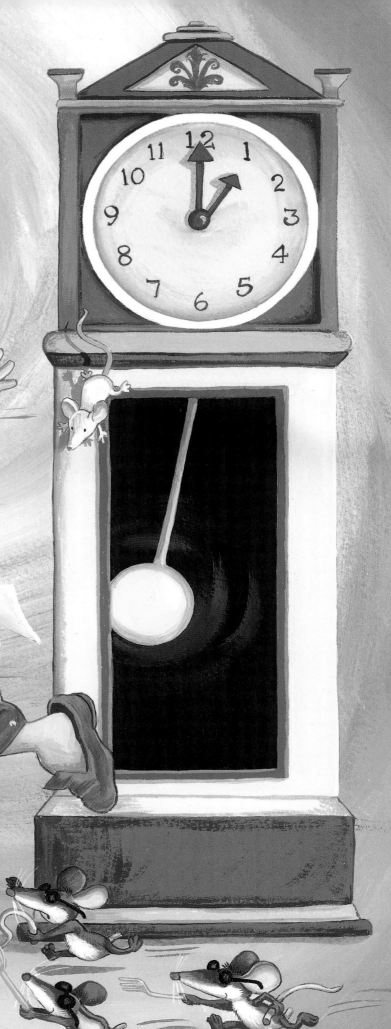

# Three Blind Mice

Three blind mice, three blind mice,
See how they run, see how they run!
They all ran after the farmer's wife,
Who cut off their tails with a carving knife,
Did you ever see such a sight in your life,
As three blind mice?

26

# This Little Piggy

This little piggy went to market,
This little piggy stayed at home,
This little piggy had roast beef,
This little piggy had none,
And this little piggy cried,
"Wee, wee, wee,"
All the way home!

# I'm A Little Teapot

I'm a little teapot, short and stout,
Here's my handle, here's my spout.
When I see the teacups, hear me shout,
"Tip me up and pour me out!"

# Little Bo-Peep

Little Bo-Peep has lost her sheep,

And doesn't know where to find them;

Leave them alone, and they'll come home,

Wagging their tails behind them.

28

# Goosey Gander

Goosey, goosey, gander,

Where shall I wander?

Upstairs and downstairs,

In my lady's chamber.

Where I met an old man,

Who wouldn't say his prayers,

So I took him by the left leg,

And threw him down the stairs.

# Here We Go Round the Mulberry Bush

Here we go round the mulberry bush,

The mulberry bush, the mulberry bush.

Here we go round the mulberry bush,

On a cold and frosty morning.

# Hey Diddle, Diddle

Hey diddle, diddle,
The cat and the fiddle,
The cow jumped over the moon.

The little dog laughed
To see such sport,
And the dish ran away
With the spoon.

# The Grand Old Duke of York

Oh, the grand old Duke of York,

He had ten thousand men;

He marched them up to the top of the hill,

And he marched them down again.

When they were up, they were up,

And when they were down, they were down,

And when they were only halfway up,

They were neither up nor down.

## Little Bird

Once I saw a little bird
Come hop, hop, hop;
So I cried, "Little bird,
Will you stop, stop, stop?"
I was going to the window
To say, "How do you do?"
But he shook his little tail,
And far away he flew.

## Peter, Peter, Pumpkin Eater

Peter, Peter, pumpkin eater,
Had a wife and couldn't keep her.
He put her in a pumpkin shell,
And there he kept her very well!

# Ring-a-Ring O' Roses

Ring-a-ring o' roses
A pocket full of posies,

"A-tishoo!
A-tishoo!"
We all fall down!

# One, Two, Three, Four, Five

One, two, three, four, five.
Once I caught a fish alive,
Six, seven, eight, nine, ten,
Then I let it go again.

Why did you let it go?
Because it bit my finger so.
Which finger did it bite?
This little finger on the right.

# Bobby Shaftoe

Bobby Shaftoe went to sea,
Silver buckles on his knee;
He'll come back and marry me,
Bonny Bobby Shaftoe!

# Humpty Dumpty

Humpty Dumpty sat on a wall,

Humpty Dumpty had a great fall.

All the King's horses

And all the King's men,

Couldn't put Humpty together again.

# Cobbler, Cobbler

Cobbler, cobbler, mend my shoe,
Get it done by half past two;
Stitch it up, and stitch it down,
And I'll give you a half a crown.

# I Had a Little Nut Tree

I had a little nut tree, nothing would it bear

But a silver nutmeg and a golden pear;

The King of Spain's daughter came to visit me,

And all for the sake of my little nut tree.

# The Crooked Man

There was a crooked man
And he walked a crooked mile,
He found a crooked sixpence
Against a crooked stile;
He bought a crooked cat,
Which caught a crooked mouse,
And they all lived together
In a little crooked house.

# Cock-a-Doodle Doo!

Cock-a-doodle doo!
My dame has lost her shoe,
My master's lost his fiddle stick,
And knows not what to do.

# Rub-a-Dub-Dub

Rub-a-dub-dub,

Three men in a tub,

And who do you think they be?

The butcher, the baker,

The candlestick-maker,

And up they jump all three!

# Round and Round the Garden

Round and round the garden

Like a teddy bear.

One step, two steps,

Tickle you under there.

# Oranges and Lemons

Oranges and lemons, say the bells of St. Clement's.

You owe me five farthings, say the bells of St. Martin's.

When will you pay me? say the bells of Old Bailey.

When I grow rich, say the bells of Shoreditch.

When will that be? say the bells of Stepney.

I do not know, say the great bells of Bow.

Here comes a candle to light you to bed.

Here comes a chopper to chop off your head.

# Simple Simon

Simple Simon met a pieman going to the fair;

Said Simple Simon to the pieman: "Let me taste your ware."

Said the pieman to Simple Simon: "Show me first your penny."

Said Simple Simon to the pieman: "Indeed, I have not any!"

# Sing a Song of Sixpence

Sing a song of sixpence,
A pocket full of rye;
Four and twenty blackbirds
Baked in a pie.

When the pie was opened,
The birds began to sing;
Oh wasn't that a dainty dish
To set before the king.

The king was in his counting house
Counting out his money;
The queen was in the parlour
Eating bread and honey.

The maid was in the garden
Hanging out the clothes;
When down came a blackbird
And pecked off her nose.

# This is the Way the Ladies Ride

This is the way the ladies ride,
Trit trot, trit trot.

This is the way the gentlemen ride,
A gallop, a trot, a gallop, a trot.

This is the way the farmer rides
Jiggety- jiggety-jog.

# The Lion and the Unicorn

The lion and the unicorn
Were fighting for the crown.
The lion beat the unicorn
All around the town.

Some gave them white bread,
And some gave them brown;
Some gave them plum cake,
And drummed them out of town.

47

## Jack Sprat

Jack Sprat could eat no fat,

His wife could eat no lean,

And so between them both,

They licked the platter clean.

## Little Boy Blue

Little Boy Blue,

Come blow your horn,

The sheep's in the meadow,

The cow's in the corn.

Where is the boy

Who looks after the sheep?

He's under a haystack,

Fast asleep!

# Polly Put the Kettle On

Polly put the kettle on,

Polly put the kettle on,

Polly put the kettle on,

We'll all have tea.

Sukey take it off again,

Sukey take it off again,

Sukey take it off again,

They've all gone away.

# Pussy Cat, Pussy Cat

Pussy cat, pussy cat,
Where have you been?
I've been up to London,
To visit the Queen.
Pussy cat, pussy cat,
What did you there?
I frightened a little mouse,
Under a chair.

# Doctor Foster

Doctor Foster went to Gloucester
In a shower of rain;
He stepped in a puddle,
Right up to his middle,
And never went there again.

# Little Tommy Tucker

Little Tommy Tucker
Sings for his supper.
What shall we give him?
White bread and butter.
How shall he cut it without a knife?
How will he be married without a wife?

51

# Curly Locks

Curly Locks, Curly Locks,
Will you be mine?
You shall not wash dishes,
Nor yet feed the swine;
You'll sit on a cushion
And sew a fine seam,
And feed upon strawberries,
Sugar and cream.

# Diddle, Diddle, Dumpling

Diddle, diddle, dumpling, my son John, went to bed with his trousers on;
One shoe off, and one shoe on, diddle, diddle, dumpling, my son John!

# To Market, To Market

To market, to market, to buy a fat pig,

Home again, home again, jiggety-jig.

To market, to market, to buy a fat hog,

Home again, home again, jiggety-jog.

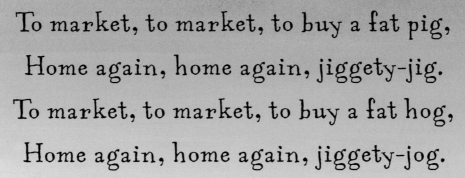

# London Bridge

London Bridge is falling down,
Falling down, falling down.

London Bridge is falling down,
My fair Lady.

Build it up with bricks and mortar,
Bricks and mortar, bricks and mortar.
Build it up with bricks and mortar,
My fair Lady.

Bricks and mortar will not stay,
Will not stay, will not stay,
Bricks and mortar will not stay,
My fair Lady.

Build it up with iron and steel,
Iron and steel, iron and steel,
Build it up with iron and steel,
My fair Lady.

Iron and steel will bend and bow,
Bend and bow, bend and bow,
Iron and steel will bend and bow,
My fair Lady.

London Bridge is falling down,
Falling down, falling down.
London Bridge is falling down,
My fair Lady.

# As I Was Going to St Ives

As I was going to St. Ives, I met a man with seven wives.

Each wife had seven sacks, each sack had seven cats,

Each cat had seven kits: kits, cats, sacks and wives,

How many were going to St. Ives?

St. Ives

# Row, Row, Row Your Boat

Row, row, row your boat,
Gently down the stream.
Merrily, merrily, merrily, merrily,
Life is but a dream.

### It's Raining, It's Pouring

It's raining, it's pouring,
The old man is snoring.
He went to bed
And bumped his head,
And couldn't get up
In the morning!

### Higgledy, Piggledy

Higgledy Piggledy, my black hen,
She lays eggs for gentlemen;

Sometimes nine,
And sometimes ten,
Higgledy Piggledy,
My black hen.

# Little Tommy Tittlemouse

Little Tommy Tittlemouse
Lived in a little house;
He caught fishes
In other mens' ditches.

# Horsey, Horsey

Horsey, horsey don't you stop,
Just let your feet go clippetty-clop.

The tail goes swish and the wheels go round
Giddy up, we're homeward bound.

# Hush Little Baby

Hush, little baby, don't say a word,
Mama's going to buy you a mockingbird.

If that mockingbird won't sing,

Mama's going to buy you a diamond ring.

If that diamond ring turns brass,

Mama's going to buy you a looking glass.

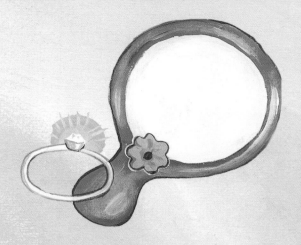

If that looking glass gets broke,

Mama's going to buy you a billy goat.

If that billy goat won't pull,

Mama's going to buy you a cart and bull.

If that cart and bull turn over,

Mama's going to buy you a dog named Rover.

If that dog named Rover won't bark,

Mama's going to buy you a horse and cart.

If that horse and cart fall down,

You'll still be the sweetest little baby in town.

# To Bed, To Bed

"To bed, to bed!" said Sleepy Head.

"Tarry a while," said Slow.

"Put on the pan," said Greedy Ann.

"We'll sup before we go."

# Twinkle, Twinkle, Little Star

Twinkle, twinkle, little star,

How I wonder what you are!

Up above the world so high,

Like a diamond in the sky.

Twinkle, twinkle, little star,

How I wonder what you are!

# Little Miss Muffet

Little Miss Muffet

Sat on a tuffet,

Eating her curds and whey;

Along came a spider,

Who sat down beside her,

And frightened Miss Muffet away.